THE GREAT BIG FUNNY BOOK

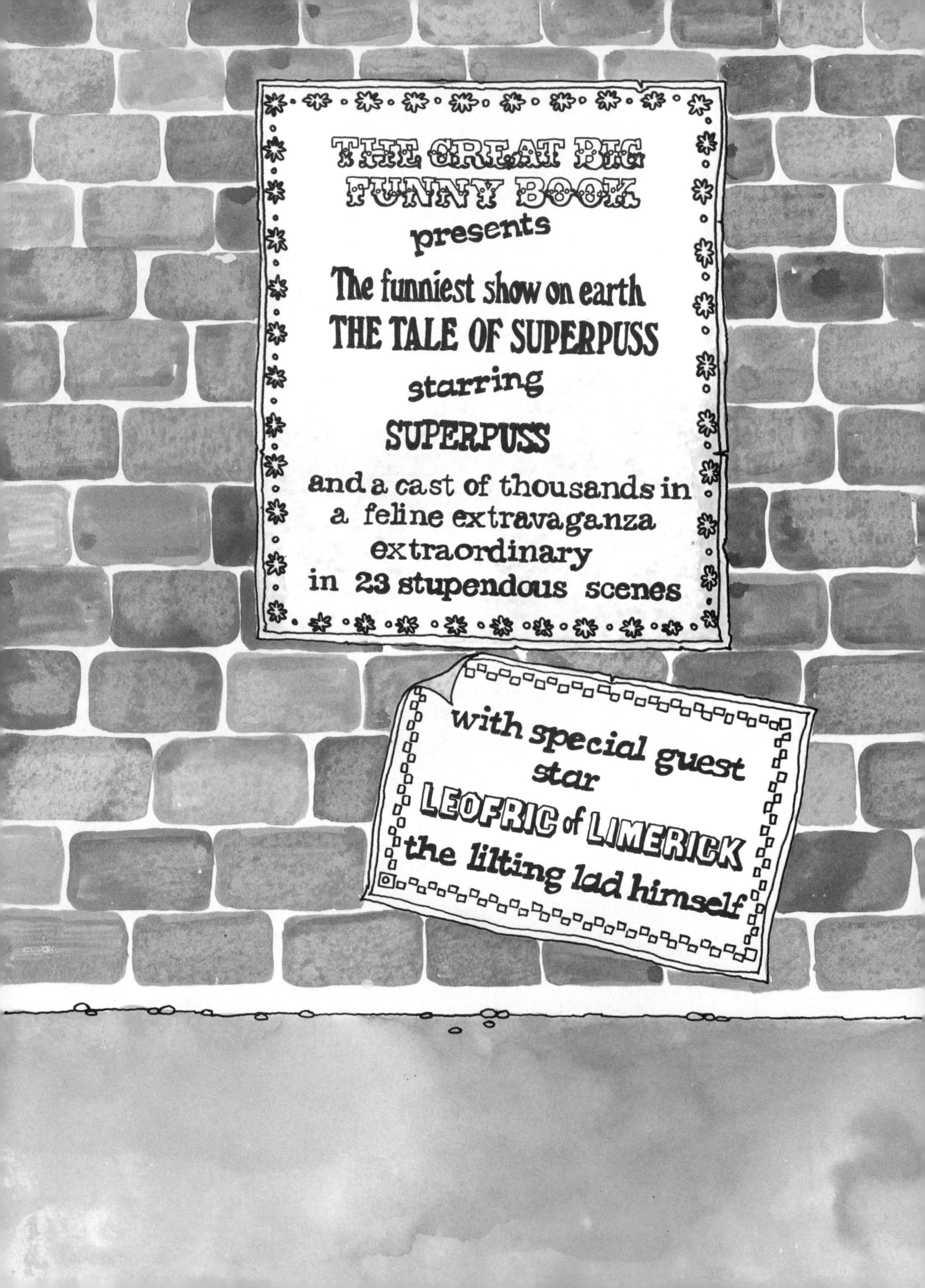
THE GREAT BIG
FUNNY BOOK
presents
The funniest show on earth
THE TALE OF SUPERPUSS
starring
SUPERPUSS
and a cast of thousands in
a feline extravaganza
extraordinary
in 23 stupendous scenes
with special guest
star
LEOFRIC of LIMERICK
the lilting lad himself

written and devised
by
GYLES
'make 'em laugh'
BRANDRETH
Designed and
illustrated by
ANN
"what a pretty"
picture
AXWORTHY
under the personal
supervision of
GILLIAN
"cor blimey!"
OSBAND
Produced and
Published by
Transworld
no expense spared
Publishers

THE GREAT BIG FUNNY BOOK
A CORGI-CAROUSEL BOOK 0·552 98050 1

First published in Great Britain in 1978

PRINTING HISTORY
Corgi-Carousel Edition published 1978

Corgi-Carousel Books are published by
Transworld Publishers Ltd.
Century House,
61–63 Uxbridge Road,
Ealing, London W.5.
Printed in Great Britain by
Redwood Burn Limited, Trowbridge & Esher

Scene 1
HERE COMES SUPERPUSS!
Can I ask you something?
Yes.
Are you comfortable?
Yes.
Can you see alright?
Yes.
Can I swap seats with you then?

Is it a Supersonic Sausage?
Is it a jet-propelled sofa?
Is it the man in the moon?
Is it his wife?
I didn't know the man in the moon had a wife.
Is it a bird?
Is it a kite?
Is it a kestrel?
Is it Kojak's barber?
Is it a supersonic carrot?
Is it Queen Elizabeth II
Is it an elephant?
Is it a Jumbo jet?
That's what I said!
Is it King Kong

Is it
Prince
Charming?
NO —IT'S SUPERPUSS!

There was a young lady of Lynn
Who was so exceedingly thin
That when she essayed
To drink lemonade
She slipped through the straw and fell in!

Scene 2
SUPERPUSS GOES TO LIVE WITH A LARGE AND LOVELY FAMILY
Do you know why Robin Hood robbed the rich?
No, why?
Because the poor didn't have anything worth taking!

Grandpa, what's a weapon?
It's something you fight with.
Is grandma your weapon?
Mummy, do you remember the vase you always worried I would break?
Yes, dear.
Well, your worries are over.
Isn't this family purrfect!
Cedric, did you fall over wearing your best trousers?
Yes, Grandma, there wasn't time to take them off.
Look, I'm letting the cat out of the bag!

Mummy, can I have some money for the old man who's crying out in the street?
Of course, dear, but what's he crying about?
He's crying, 'Try Feezo's Super Ices!'
Dad, will you help me with my sums?
No, son. It wouldn't be right.
Never mind. You could at least try.
MATHS
Dad calls me Sonny because I'm so bright.
How did Mum find out you didn't really have a bath?
I forgot to wet the soap.

There was a young fellow called Ned
Who dined before going to bed
On lobster and ham
And salad and jam—
And when he woke up he was dead!

Scene 3
SUPERPUSS GOES TO SCHOOL
So you survived the Titanic?
That's right.
But what did you do when the boat sank?
I just grabbed a bar of soap and washed myself ashore.

What do two wrongs make?
A right. But what did two wright's make?
The first aeroplane!
Psst! Sammy, what are you doing crawling in on all fours?
Teacher told me I mustn't ever dare walk in late.
I luv you
Teacher likes me. She's put a big kiss on all my work.
What's ignorance?
It's when you don't know something and somebody finds it out.
S.P.

Ba + Na² =
brain food
=noodle soup
What will you be when you leave school?
A very old man.
Jimmy, do you know what a cannibal is?
No, teacher.
Well, if you ate your mummy and daddy what would you be?
An orphan.
Dear Teache
you must no
beat little Willie.
He is a delicate
boy. We never
hit him at
home except in
self-defence.
love from
Mum
Did you hear about the cross-eyed teacher who had no control over his pupils?
LUNCH
S.P.

There was a young lady called Ruth
Who had a great passion for truth.
She said she would die
Before she would lie—
And she died in the prime of her youth!

Scene 4
SUPERPUSS
LOVES SPORT
I got onto one of those speaking weighing machines today.
Really, what did it say?
One person at a time please.

When was tennis mentioned in the Bible?
I don't know.
When Joseph served in Pharaoh's court.
I've got a terrible cold. I won't be able to do the high jump.
Why not?
I can't even clear my throat.
Why is tennis such a noisy game?
Because both players raise a racket.

I know it's dangerous to swim on a full stomach, so after lunch I always swim on my back.
Why are you wearing two pairs of trousers?
In case I make a hole in one.
SP
My name's Cinderella and I'm running away from the Prince's ball.
Are you a good loser?
I'm perfect!
5
What race always starts with a tie?
I don't know.
A three-legged race, of course.
Foiled again!
2

A railway official from Crewe
Met an engine one day that he knew
Though he smiled and he bowed
That engine was proud:
It cut him—it cut him in two!

Scene 5
SUPERPUSS ALWAYS HELPS WITH THE FAMILY SHOPPING
Say something soft and sweet.
Marshmallow.

This pair of shoes I bought from you last week is useless. One heel is shorter than the other. What do you expect me to do?
Limp!
This apple's rotten.
I don't know what you're complaining about. You only bought one. I've got hundreds!
RIPE, JUICY APPLES The early bird gets the worm
I don't like the look of this mackerel.
If it's looks you're after, why don't you buy a goldfish?

I want to try on that suit in the window.
I'm sorry, sir, but you'll have to try it on in the changing room.
I have to work as a baker. I knead the dough.
Do you serve nuts?
We serve anybody.
Butcher, what would you call a stupid pig thief?
A Hamburglar!
I'd like something green, curly and difficult to understand.
Lettuce think about it. Would you like something red, green and unwilling instead?
No, I don't like forced rhubarb!

There was a young fellow of Ealing
Endowed with such delicate feeling,
When he read on the door,
'Don't spit on the floor,'
He jumped up and spat on the ceiling!

Scene 6
SUPERPUSS GOES TO THE CIRCUS
Sometimes you remind me of the Atlantic Ocean.
Romantic, wild and restless?
No, you just make me sick.

Did you know that Sam the Strong Man had a glass eye?
Did he tell you?
No, it just came out in the conversation.
And now, ladies and gentlemen, introducing Tiny Timmy Thompson —at Five foot eleven inches, the world's tallest dwarf!
I've had a great idea for a new act.
What's that?
The lion makes friends with the dove.
What happens if they quarrel?
We get a new dove!

Why won't your pony talk today?
Because he's a little hoarse.
There was a Strong Man of Calcutta
Who had an unfortunate stutter;
At tea-time he said:
'Give me some b-b-bread
and some b-b-b-b-b-b-b-b-butter!'
MR MARVEL THE AMAZING MEMORY MAN
You know, I'm losing my memory. I'm terrified!
Don't worry. Relax and forget all about it.
Are you Fearless Freddie the fearless lion-tamer?
No. I just comb the lions and brush their teeth.

*There was an old man from Nantucket
Who kept all his cash in a bucket;
His daughter, called Nan,
Ran away with a man—
And as for the bucket, Nantucket!*

Scene 7
SUPERPUSS GOES OUT IN THE FAMILY CAR
I've changed my mind.
Fantastic! Does the new one work any better?

Is your horn broken?
No, it doesn't care.
What do you mean?
Well, it doesn't give a hoot.
I've got a baby car —it doesn't go anywhere without a rattle.
What did your father say when you told him I'd smashed the car?
Shall I leave out the swear words?
Yes, of course.
He didn't say a word.
What kind of song do you sing in a car?
A cartoon!
SP

Why is your car painted blue on one side and red on the other?
It's a great idea. You should hear the witnesses contradicting one another!
I'm going to write my automobile's life story.
Really? Will you call it your autobiography?!
At what time of day are you like the wheel of a car?
At night when you are tired!
What is the best thing to take when you are run down?
The number of the car that hit you!
I can't stand up. I'm two-tired.

There was a young lady of Crete
Who was so excessively neat,
When she got out of bed
She stood on her head
To make sure of not soiling her feet.

Scene 8
SUPERPUSS
VISITS
A FARM
When I visited a farm they had goats without horns
But—
I've just told you: there were no butts.

Why are you driving over that field with a steamroller?
I'm trying to grow mashed potatoes.
That big rooster's making eyes at me again.
You've got to stop egging him on.
Where are you going to get your hair cut?
At the baa-baa shop.
This is a dogwood tree.
How can you tell?
By its bark.
What would you get if you crossed a flea with a rabbit?
A bug's bunny!
Look—a cow's nest
SP
OINKMENT

My little boy polishes shoes in the big city.
I'm a farmer. I make hay while the son shines!
Is a chicken big enough to eat when it's two weeks old?
Of course not.
Then how does it manage to live?
Moo!
Baa-aa-a!
What do you mean 'Baa-aa-a'?
I'm learning a foreign language.
Can I ask you how long cows should be milked?
Same way as short cows, sonny.

There was a young man of Devizes
Whose ears were of different sizes.
The one that was small
Was no use at all,
But the other won several prizes.

Scene 9
THE FAMILY WHERE SUPERPUSS LIVES HAVE LOTS OF LOVELY TREATS. SOMETIMES THEY GO OUT TO A SMART RESTAURANT FOR A GRAND AND GLORIOUS FAMILY FEAST.
Our dog Fido is just like one of the family.
Which one?

This egg's bad.
Don't blame me. I only laid the table.
Eat your spinach, dear. It'll put colour into your cheeks.
Who wants green cheeks?
This coffee tastes like mud!
Well, what do you expect, sir. It was only ground this morning.
We have practically everything on the menu.
So I see. Would you bring me a clean one?

I can't eat this food. Call the manager.
There's no point, sir. He can't eat it either.
I'm afraid all this food's going to waist.
Do you like meat balls?
I don't know. I've never been to any.
Waiter, there's a dead spider in my soup.
Yes, I know, sir. It's the heat that kills them.
I don't think much of your wife.
Never mind—eat the vegetables instead.

Old Greedyguts, dining at Crewe,
Found quite a large mouse in his stew.
Said the waiter, 'Don't shout
And wave it about,
Or the rest will be wanting one too!'

Scene 10
FOR ANOTHER TREAT SUPERPUSS IS TAKEN TO THE ZOO.
What would you call an intelligent duck?
A superduck?
No. A wise quacker.

Why does a monkey scratch himself?
I don't know. Why?
Because he's the only one who knows where it itches!
I can't wait for Leap Year.
Why have I got such small appetite?
Because with you a little goes a long way.
What do you call the largest, fiercest lion in the zoo?
'Sir'!
I don't give a hoot about anything.
If you crossed a kangaroo with a sheep you'd get a woolly jumper.
I think I've got a person in my throat.

Why shouldn't you cry when a cow falls on the ice?
Because it's no use crying over spilt milk.
How can I get the rabbit to come out of its hutch?
Make a noise like a carrot.
What do you call a camel with three humps?
Humphrey.
What do kangaroos have that no other animals have?
Little kangaroos.

A cheerful old bear at the zoo
Could always find something to do.
When it bore him, you know,
To walk to and fro,
He reversed it, and walked fro and to.

Scene 11
SUPERPUSS GOES TO HOSPITAL TO HAVE HIS TONSILS TAKEN OUT.
What bird can lift the heaviest weights?
The crane!

Nurse, have you got anything for my liver?
Only onions.
Here is Dr. Cholmondley-Funk-Fiennes to see you.
Which doctor?
Oh, no, he's fully qualified.
Why aren't you taking the cough medicine I gave you?
I tasted the medicine and decided I'd rather have the cough!
Nurse, nurse, I've just swallowed a spoon!
Sit down and don't stir.
That surgeon's so funny he's got me in stitches!

Doctor, my hair keeps falling out. Have you got anything to keep it in?
A cardboard box.
What did the tonsil say to the other tonsil?
I don't know. What?
Get dressed. The doctor's taking us out tonight!
Why do we wear these masks?
So that if one of us makes a mistake no-one will know who did it.
Have your eyes ever been checked?
No, they've always been blue.

INTERVAL
WILL SUPERPUSS COME OUT OF HOSPITAL ALIVE?
WILL SUPERPUSS LEAVE HOME AND TRAVEL ROUND THE WORLD?
WILL SUPERPUSS FIND A NEW FRIEND FOR LIFE AND GO ON A THOUSAND AND ONE EXCITING ADVENTURES?
You Bet He Will!
Have a piece of chocolate.
Thanks. It's delicious.
Yes, I know. It's like you: half nuts.

Scene 12
SUPERPUSS–
WITHOUT HIS TONSILS–
COMES OUT OF HOSPITAL AND AS
A WELL-DONE-YOU-GOT-WELL
PRESENT THE FAMILY
TAKE HIM TO BUY
A PET.
DOG
That was a short interval.
Time flies when you are enjoying yourself.
Time flies? You can't. They fly too fast.

GENTLE DOG FOR SALE.
HOUSE TRAINED.
WILL EAT ANYTHING.
SPECIALLY FOND OF
CHILDREN.
What should I give the budgie for breakfast?
Shredded tweet.
Bonzo wants me to take him to see the film *Jaws*.
Well, I am surprised!
I'm surprised too—he didn't like the book at all.
You're the dog for me. My name's Superpuss. What's yours?
I'm not sure, but I think its Down Boy.

My dog swallowed a light bulb yesterday.
Did it choke him?
Oh, no, he spat it out at once.
So now he's de-lighted!
Have you given the goldfish fresh water today?
No. They haven't finished what I gave them yesterday.
I'm a sourpuss.

There was a young lady of Kent
Whose nose was most awfully bent.
She followed her nose
One day, I suppose—
And no-one knows which way she went!

Scene 13
SUPERPUSS AND DOWN BOY LEAVE HOME AND DECIDE TO TRAVEL THE WORLD.
What's the difference between a cat and a comma?
A cat has claws at the end of its paws and a comma has a pause at the end of its clause!

What's your name, sir?
Sneeze.
Is that a Chinese name?
No, that's my name in English.
What's your name in Chinese?
Ah Choo!
Bless you.
Does this train stop at Grand Central Station?
Well, there'll be a terrible crash if it doesn't.
I'm glad I wasn't born in China.
Why?
I can't speak a word of Chinese.
I just flew in from New York.
Your arms must be exhausted.

Dad, have you ever been to Egypt?
No, son, why?
Well, where did you get Mummy?
Is this a picture of my bus?
No, sir, it belongs to the company.
Don't be stupid. I mean is this the bus I'm going to take to Edinburgh?
No, sir, it's far too heavy.
Why does Nelson's Column stand in Trafalgar Square?
Because it can't sit down.
Do ships this size sink very often?
No, madam. Never more than once.

There was a young lady of Cork,
Whose Pa made a fortune in pork,
He bought for his daughter
A tutor who taught her
To balance green peas on her fork

Scene 14
SUPERPUSS AND DOWN BOY ARRIVE IN THE JUNGLE.
How can a leopard change his spots?
By moving!

Can you think of an animal that's a cannibal?
A horse. It eats it's fodder.
Where do baby apes sleep?
In apricots.
Are we going to meet the King of the Jungle?
I haven't made an appointment.
Why not?
Every time I called I got the same answer; lion's engaged.
Where does a two ton gorilla sleep?
Anywhere it wants!
What do you give a sick rhinoceros?
Plenty of room!
SP

Can you name ten African animals in 10 seconds?
Four giraffes and six zebras.
I love cocoa.
I'm a coconut too!
What Christmas song do you like best?
Jungle bells! Jungle bells!
Come on, play fair!
Why should I? I'm a cheetah!

The bottle of perfume that Willie sent
Was highly displeasing to Millicent.
Her thanks were so cold
They quarrelled, I'm told,
Through that silly scent Willie sent Millicent.

Scene 15
SUPERPUSS AND DOWN BOY MEET THE ELEPHANTS.
Why do cows wear cowbells?
Because their horns don't work.

Why is an elephant large, grey and wrinkled?
Because if he was small, white and round he'd be an aspirin.
What time is it when the elephant sits on the roof of your car?
Time to get a new car.
How do you get down off an elephant?
You don't. You get down off a duck.
What would you get if you crossed an elephant with a mouse?
Huge holes in the wall.

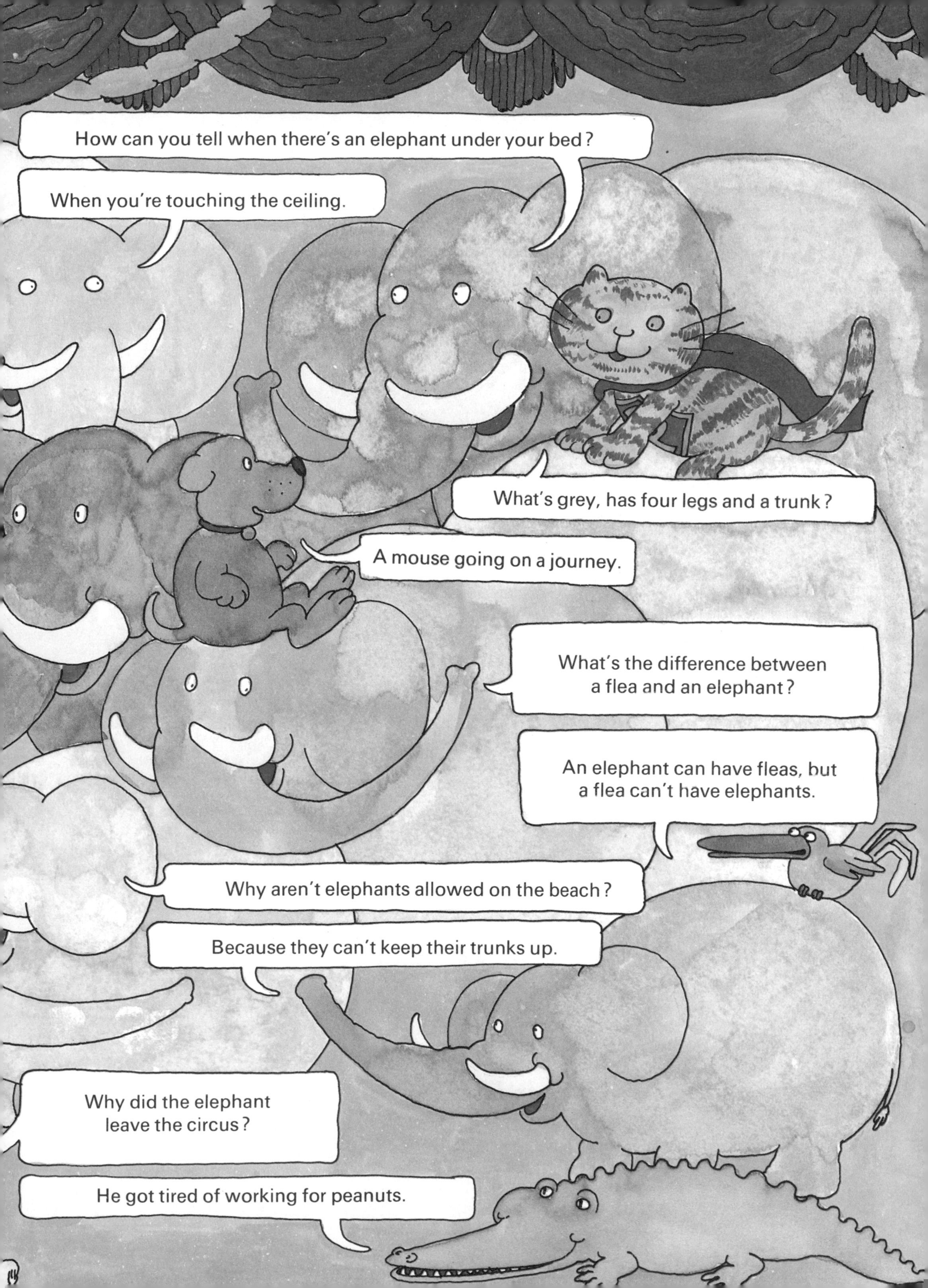

How can you tell when there's an elephant under your bed?
When you're touching the ceiling.
What's grey, has four legs and a trunk?
A mouse going on a journey.
What's the difference between a flea and an elephant?
An elephant can have fleas, but a flea can't have elephants.
Why aren't elephants allowed on the beach?
Because they can't keep their trunks up.
Why did the elephant leave the circus?
He got tired of working for peanuts.

*A mouse in her room woke Miss Dowd,
She was frightened—it must be allowed.
Soon a happy thought hit her
To scare off the critter:
She sat up in bed and meowed!*

Scene 16
AFTER HIS WORLD TOUR, SUPERPUSS DECIDES TO SETTLE DOWN AND GET A JOB. HE WANTS TO BE AN ARTIST, SO OFF HE GOES TO ART SCHOOL.
What is a HIbVE?
It's a small bee in a big hive.

And will I look beautiful in the painting?
Oh, yes. You won't recognise yourself.
That's stupid. Anyone can see he's by himself.
REMBRANDT
~by himself.
This is a picture of a cow grazing.
Where's the grass?
The cow's eaten it.
Where's the cow?
You don't expect her to hang around once she's eaten all the grass, do you?
Why did they hang that picture?
Because they couldn't find the artist.

"Old Master"
Old Missus
When I look at your paintings I stand and wonder—
How I do it?
No. **Why** do you do it?
Do you ever draw pictures in the nude?
No, I always wear a smock.
And this monstrosity is what they call Modern Art, is it?
No. It's a mirror.
SP

A painter who lived in West Ditting,
Interrupted two girls with their knitting.
He said, with a sigh,
'That park bench—well I
Just painted it, right where you're sitting!'

Scene 17
SUPERPUSS FAILS AS AN ARTIST AND DECIDES TO BECOME A SCIENTIST INSTEAD.
What's the last word in airplanes?
JUMP!

What does HNO_3 stand for?
It's on the tip of my tongue.
Well, spit it out at once! It's nitric acid!
What did the amoeba say to the protoplasm?
Don't bacilli!
Why did the germ cross the microscope?
To get to the other slide.
Light travels at the rate of 186,000 miles per second.
that's nothing — it's downhill all the way.

An apple dropping on his head
Set Newton thinking, but—
The story might have had another end
Had it been a coconut!
I have at last discovered an acid
that will eat up **everything**.
That's fantastic—but what
are you going to keep it in?
This gas is so dangerous,
what steps should we take
if it escapes?
Large ones.
What do you get if
you swallow uranium?
A-tomic ache.

A Major, with a wonderful force,
Called out in Hyde Park for a horse.
All the flowers looked round,
But no horse could be found,
So he just rhododendrun, of course!

Scene 18
SUPERPUSS FAILS AS A SCIENTIST AND GOES TO WORK IN A GRAND HOTEL.
What did the painter say to the wall?
One more crack like that and I'll plaster you.

Can you give me a room and bath?
I can give you a room, madam, but you'll have to give yourself the bath.
Does this hotel have 24 hour room service?
Yes, it takes 24 hours to serve you!
Telegram for Mr. Frizzlegrapplebaum! Telegram for Mr. Frizzlegrapplebaum!
What initial, please?
Did you ring, madam?
No, I was tolling. I thought you were dead.

The flies are certainly thick around here.
Yes, they're not very intelligent, are they?
Here are some views of our hotel for you to take away as souvenirs, sir.
Thank you, but I have my own views of your hotel!
All our mattresses are stuffed with the best straw.
Now I know where they got the straw that broke the camel's back.
There's water pouring through the ceiling of my bedroom!
Of course, sir. There's running water in every room.
Does the water always come through the roof like this?
Oh no, sir. Only when it rains.

A tutor who taught on the flute
Tried to teach two young tooters to toot.
Said the two to the tutor,
'Is it harder to toot, or
To tutor two tooters to toot?'

Scene 19
SUPERPUSS LEAVES THE GRAND HOTEL AND OPENS A BARBER SHOP.
What do you call a monkey who loves fish and chips?
A fish and chip monk.

Were you wearing a red scarf when you came in?
No.
Then I must have cut your throat!
SUPERPUS
the
BARBER
it's a snip
Your hair is thinning, sir. Have you ever tried one of our special Superpuss Preparations?
No, I can't blame it on that.
Your hair needs cutting badly.
That's why I come here. They always cut it badly.

And how did you like the razor?
I didn't know I was being shaved.
I'm delighted.
I thought I was being sandpapered.
And how would you like your hair cut, son?
Just like my dad's—and don't forget the little round hole at the top where the head comes through.
National Union of Hairdressers
BARBERS TO GET FRINGE BENEFITS
This is a hair-raising story!
Your dog seems to enjoy watching you cut hair.
It isn't that. Sometimes I snip off a bit of the customer's ear.

There was a young lady of Rhyde
Who ate a green apple and died.
The apple fermented
Inside the lamented,
And made cider inside her inside.

Scene 20
SUPERPUSS'S BARBER'S SHOP IS A FAILURE, SO HE TURNS IT INTO A DENTIST'S SHOP INSTEAD!
What's the world's longest piece of furniture?
The multiplication table.

SUPERPUS
the dentist who's
quick on the dr
That wasn't the tooth I wanted out!
Calm yourself, my man.
I'm just coming to it.
Why did you just hit me?
Because you got on my nerves!
A-a-a-a-h!
You needn't open your
mouth any wider. I'm
planning to extract
your tooth from out-
side!

Do you extract teeth painlessly?
Not always. Yesterday I twisted my wrist quite badly!
When I have to have false teeth I want that pair.
Stop it, Elliott. You know it's not polite to pick your teeth in public.
Do you swear to pull the tooth, the whole tooth and nothing but the tooth?
Funny, I thought he was supposed to be painless.

There was an old fellow called Green
Who grew so abnormally lean,
And flat and compressed,
That his back touched his chest,
And sideways he couldn't be seen!

Scene 21
SUPERPUSS FAILS AS A DENTIST, SO HE BECOMES A PROFESSIONAL BOXER INSTEAD.
What did the tie say to the hat?
You go on ahead, I'll just hang around.

Hit him! Hit him!
Not with that, you fool!
I called you this morning and your wife said you weren't up yet.
I've got a cabbage nose, cauliflower ears, and between my nose and chin: tulips!
SP
Have I hurt him yet?
No, but keep swinging your arms about. The breeze might give him a cold.

BRIMSTOWN BOXING CLUB
Colours: black and blue
That's what's called a half hook—
Well, you can keep the other half!
It's force of habit: I never get up before the stroke of ten.
It's a positive insult.
It's a long way from the dressing-room to the ring, isn't it?
Don't worry, you won't have to walk back.

There was a young lady from Australia
Who went to a dance as a dahlia !
When the petals uncurled,
They revealed to the world,
That the dress, as a dress, was a failure.

Scene 22
SUPERPUSS FAILS
AS A BOXER
AND DECIDES
TO BECOME
A POET INSTEAD.
When do ghosts have most fun?
When they're in high spirits!

There was an old man from Leeds
Who swallowed a packet of seeds
A large geranium grew out of his cranium
And his eyelids were covered with weeds.

There was a young lady of Spain
Who was terribly sick in the train
Not once, but again and again
And again and again and again.

Humpty Dumpty sat on a wall.
Humpty Dumpty had a great fall.
All the King's horses and all the King's men
Came and ate scrambled eggs on toast.

I love to stand upon my head
And think of things sublime
Until my mother interrupts
And says it's dinner-time.

A peanut sat on the railroad track
His heart was all a flutter
Along came a train, the 8.15—
Toot, toot, peanut butter!

It's easy enough to be pleasant
When life flows round and round,
But the man worth while
Is the man who can smile
With his trousers falling down!

There was an old man of Peru
Who really had nothing to do,
So he sat on the stairs
And counted his hairs,
And found he had seventy-two.

FINALE
Scene 23
AT LONG LAST, SUPERPUSS FINDS SUCCESS. HIS POETRY IS ACCLAIMED THROUGHOUT THE WORLD. HE IS HERALDED AS THE GREATEST POET HISTORY HAS EVER KNOWN. HE HAS A CRESCENT IN PONDERS END NAMED AFTER HIM AND BECOMES POET LAUREATE.
HE ALSO GOES TO BUCKINGHAM PALACE TO BE KNIGHTED BY HER MAJESTY THE QUEEN.
Why is a cloak like a banana skin?
Because both are easy to slip on!

I'm being knighted, too.
What for?
I invented spaghetti.
Really, how?
I used my noodle.
What are you being knighted for?
I write spooky horror stories.
Oh, you're a ghost writer.
I'm a footman.
Whenever I'm down in the dumps, I get a new hat.
Oh, so that's where you find them.

I'm going to be a lord, you know.
What's your name?
Boo.
Boo who?
Oh, please don't cry.
Your umbrella looks as if it's seen better days.
Yes, it's had its ups and downs.
Arise, Sir Superpuss!
This is the end of his tale.
I'm a feetman.

A triumph!
Super!
Well done!
Incredible!
Magnifique!
Encore!
Miraculous!
Hilarious!
Wunderbar!
Three cheers for Ann Axworthy!
Author! Author!
Fantastic!
What did you think of it?
Not bad, but I preferred **Hamlet**.
A hit!